Little Chimp and Big Chimp

Story by Jenny Giles
Illustrations by Rachel Tonkin

Little Chimp is going

up in the trees.

Little Chimp is going

up and down.

Big Chimp is asleep

in the sun.

Little Chimp is going

up and down,

up and down.

Little Chimp is going
up to the big tree.

Oh, no!

Down comes Little Chimp.

Big Chimp wakes up.

Big Chimp is looking

for Little Chimp.

Little Chimp is up

in the big tree.